Advancec

MW00779370

This book comprises pyrotechnics of text that retain a solid elevation to severe displacements of space and time. This books contains cadavers on a thrill ride who are mining the alphabet to take pleasure in ... and endorse ... the unpredictability of meaning. Submerge yourself ... dear reader ... in redacted text that acts as possible photography ... the author requests you to view him through black ink ... through potential black smoke that turns as a scrying assistant. Mike Corrao has written a great book ... my kind of book ... a book that is on the verge of collapse where various pages depict asemic pictograms ... where scrapings from past art and literature manifestoes assemble a new structure that defiles the past.

— Shane Jesse Christmass, author of *Belfie Hell*

A disquieting and strangely beautiful exploration of text-as-entity. As Corrao's creatures wrestle with their various states of being (or non-being), their yearnings toward the corporeal reflect humanity's yearnings toward the spiritual: a desire to become something greater than their state allows. Ultimately, *Gut Text* challenges the reader to question the integrity of their own sentience and corporeality, suggesting that existence is merely a choice, and one born out of vanity rather than an inherent virtue.

— B.R. Yeager, author of *Amygdalatropolis*

Ex-forming un-formation, not yet a map but an abstract sketch of vectors indicating how to draw a set of infrathin Borgesian labyrinths, epigenetics longing for a genome, embryogenesis in search of a dank embryo, Mike Corrao's *Gut Text* is a schizoanalytically-disconstructed Beckettian dream dreaming itself, an infestation of two-letter viruses poetically exploring their own bioplastic dreamscape. Avant-theory-fiction at its best, Corrao's book develops as a morphospatial field of dysphoric atopias ("Every variation of me is a new entity inhabiting this mobile assemblage") imbued with an odic force which pursues the chance of becoming organic without organs ("should I be made organismally, or would you allow me to build myself out of new parts?"). Like the depsyched collective eros of soldier ants gathering to form a colony-body, the text morphs into an implausible code-spell of mineral-to-living dialectic vibration—an enticement to abandon yourself to the invasion of a multitude of typefaced parasites orbiting each other in epiexperimental gravitational speculation, awaiting, with the demonic patience of text-love, to flagella-latch your white-noised environment into unbearable gut joy.

— Germán Sierra, author of *The Artifact*

In his second book, Mike Corrao again takes the oath of black blood, rendering in ink what can only be in ink, a book pure in its bookness.

— John Trefry, author of *Apparitions of the Living*

Mike Corrao's *Gut Text* is a formal experiment in abstraction, a ride into language plucked from the mouth of its maker. Not for the faint of heart, this book writhes under the reader's gaze in a compelling dance punctuated by moments of shocking aesthetic clarity.

— Tatiana Ryckman, author of *I Don't Think of You (Until I Do)*

Gut Text reminds me of the sort of fiction I absolutely love to read; one where there is no knowing exactly what is going to happen next—everything and nothing, all at the same time, makes absolute sense. Think of it as a sort of chewing up and then spitting out of whatever you can think up and / or imagine (covered in bitumen and bile, of course)! Seriously—in *Gut Text*, Corrao creates an anthropology of the parallel dimension that exists only on the periphery of what we know / perceive as normal. I hope that after the world has ended and we've all melted back into a primordial goop, *Gut Text* is also destroyed; only because it paints the portrait of a terrifying place and time no one should ever desire to exist. Conceptually, there is an interesting sort of ruin that occurs, as the novel progresses—and you begin to realize that what is actually happening is a derealisation / collapse of reality. I could see someone saying, "Read between the lines and you'll begin to understand the text," but after page 13, there are no lines! It's like howling at the moon, except the moon doesn't exist and you are something that shouldn't even be. I would say this is surrealist literature with a purpose, but it's more than that even (as Surrealism itself can be so limiting). It's a Dave Markson-style mashup (which I love) with bits of Bolaño sprinkled about and then doused and set afire in an extremely well-contained but severely smoked-out Ashbery-esque kerosene fire. I experienced pareidolia multiple times while reading *Gut Text*—some of the more abstract moments caused allowed me to see images where images were not! The idea of multiple discovery assumes there is no such thing as the original idea from just one individual. For any great work or discovery, there has to be that other person (or set of persons) doing the same thing. Well… I don't know that I have yet seen or read anything else out there that is quite like *Gut Text* by Mike Corrao.

— Mike Kleine, author of *Lonely Men Club* and *Kanley Stubrick*

GUT TEXT

Maggie,

Thanks so much for coming out and for
reading this cursed object. I hope that
you enjoy it & that it does not
haunt to you for the rest of your
days.

GUT

TEXT

BY

MIKE CORRAO

GUT TEXT

Copyright © 2019 by Mike Corrao

All rights reserved.

This book may not be reproduced in whole or in part, except for the inclusion of brief quotations in a review, without permission in writing from the author or publisher. No part of this publication may be reproduced, stored in or introduced into retrieval system, or transmitted, in any form, or by any means (electronic, mechanical, photocopying, recording, or otherwise), without prior permission of the publisher. Requests for permission should be directed to 1111@1111press.com, or mailed to 11:11 Press LLC, 4757 15th Ave S., Minneapolis, MN 55407

LCCN: 2018959930

978-1-948687-05-8 (paperback)

978-1-948687-06-5 (ebook)

FIRST AMERICAN EDITION

Printed in the United States of America

9 8 7 6 5 4 3 2 1

CONTENTS

ACKNOWLEDGMENTS

Andrew Wilt, James Habiger, Jennifer Greidus, Chris Dankland, Arielle Tipa, Patty Corrao, Joe Corrao, Ari Newman, Daymian Snowden, Logan Jones.

The TEXT would like to acknowledge Occulum and X-R-A-Y for publishing select pieces of itself in its primitive form.

[nn has the desire to disappear. To shift from their existence as text, into a place where the corporeal is torn apart. Molecules split. Nucleus diffuse into its surrounding tissue]

[nn recognizes disappearing is incredibly easy. All they have to do is stop. STOP. Doing what they are doing. All they have to do is stop. STOP. Moving and let the text roll forward on its own. So simple. But nn is a coward]

[Cowards are slow to disappear. The weight of nothingness is much more to bear than the weight of thingness. nn has already grown accustomed to the weight of thingness. Even now. So early in their existence. nn recognizes their own thingness]

[nn decides the act of disappearing begins with a complete understanding of their own thingness. Of everything it is comprised of. They form a list]

[But then the list falls apart and they do not know how to put it back together]

[nn not speaking. nn on the edge of formation. Crossing into existence. Existent. A corporeal something. Here now. Text breathing and clenched tight muscle]

[nn materialized and incapable of escape. The rhizome of my making. nn locked in strata. The full body of pages and pages of girth. Wide and alive]

[nn is alive]

[Here and alive. Of shape. Of context. Of biology. Organismal and thinking. The body made of organic materials turned inorganic. Conceived in the bath of chemicals. Born in bleach. Alive and here]

[Shapely erotica. Too concerned to die, but wanting to die. Not a narrator. I am not a narrator. I am not inside. I am. This is my body and you are reading the veins that carry my blood]

[Existent without metaphor or metonym. In the act of existing. Simple and straightforward. This is the crust of my self]

[nn wants to disappear but does not have the courage to do it. So we are here. In the act of defining my self. Witness my construction. The body electric. Digital and tactile. In multitudes. The duplicable existence]

[nn is alive, but something more complicated is going on here]

[Language is an act of possession. I am not my self. There is another hand at work here. The malicious something. Thingness stretched through a filter. The filter made of flesh and fragile. The filter a type of delirium. Raving hysterical]

[nn entering the corporeal realm and feeling like they need to vomit. Heat onset from formation. Tones locked within the larynx. Tongue fused to the roof of my mouth. There are things I am incapable of saying. Words incapable of forming in the crevasses of my throat]

[nn approaches the idea of non-existence at the realization of the non-biological nature of their thingness]

[Will you look at me? You cannot help it. Look at me. See the contents of my construction. See the archaic mother of my making. Rhizome as it devours the arborescent. Pools of liquid. Ink or water or blood or pus. Or my vomit. Have I found the capacity to vomit? No nono. I have not found my roots]

[nn with the desire to exist in a real place with real thingness. Biological. Organic. Finite in the crawling teleological. Made of softer tissue. Tiny objects put together in the hopes of forming a subject]

[Vocal and attractive. Mobile and compartmentalized]

[But hopeless. There is no transition. No strata to move across. Bringing text to organism. In this recognition there is also a recognition of the original desire, and a recognition of the desire's inaccessibility. nn is a coward]

[nn alive without any certainty in the approach towards reversal]

[who is ff / yy / vv and what does ff / yy / vv entail? What is this material made of and what can it be used to build? What collage? What is the product of subjects put together, as objects put together to form subjects]

[Objects::Subject]

[Subjects:: ███████████]

[nn witnessing the creation of every existent. nn watching Ovid's metamorphosis into something resembling an organism]

[ff::something]

[yy::large]

[vv::large]

[nn as the data which collected in this particular place. nn as a filing cabinet. nn as a storage shed in the middle of the· woods. nn as boxes full of objects which might as well not exist at all]

[nn in search of lost meanings]

[nn examining the possibilities of their ontology]

. . . .
. . . .
. . . .
. . . .
. . . .
. . . .
. . . .
. . .   .

[Then heaving onto the ground and fantasizing about what it might feel like to have a body. Sweet organism. The flesh clinging to the dense papier-mâché frame. Sturdy fragile shapely something. Descriptive and dead at the moment it's touched]

[nn pretending to be real. Saying, "don't touch me. I'll die." And then collapsing onto the floor. Fantasizing about how cold the floor would be if they could collapse onto it]

[nn approaching this moment. Where they have to ask what kind of physical pleasure they could allot themself. Or what kind of fantasies they can pretend are not fantasies]

[nn with fantasies of falling onto the floor and reaching their newly grown limbs from corner to corner]

[nn in the midst of this new dreamscape. The astral projection of a living text. Livid organism]

[DREAMSCAPE: A sea of erotic figures. Sweet, honey-like bodies tied together in fluid arches. A pattern of yonic and phallic designs, and any variations thereof. Where the movements of genitalia are independent and adrift. The slow decay of something nn has never participated in. Then the extreme pleasure of the something as it drags across their skin. The arch of their bones. Bones made from papier-mâché, with meat tightly gripped around them. nn in the bed of erotic pleasure where their thingness becomes beautiful and satisfying. The blood of a poet poured into the mouth, flowing down the esophagus and into the belly until it is full and pooling. Running along the seams of the face and into the origin from which these patterns have radiated. nn in the moment of desire fulfilled, where they feel nothing, but accept this nothing as a kind of small victory. A lapse in time between one desire and the next. The desire to recognize a second desire]

....
....
....
....
....
....
....
....

[nn a lapse in time]

....
....
....
....
....
....
....
....

....
....
....
....
....
....
....
....

[a lapse in time alarms nn]

[time takes on the qualities of space. nn realizes they need space to exist. If nn is not placed somewhere within their environment, there is no existence. And each moment without space is a lapse in time]

[nn reconsiders the modes of their existence. The desire to exist. Desires to disappear. The pain of fading into the aether. Shivering flesh and a return to the softness of corporeality]

[Object made out of somethings. Eorirhnroeprijfnfofpdij-fokrinh in a room full of *this*. Trying to latch its tendrils onto the surface]

[Then the realization these surfaces cannot be latched on-to. They must be reassessed]

[The shapely something as it crawls into the corpse of an abstract machine. Roots slither into the notches of each gear. Incomprehensible geometries. Long droplets of wa-ter. Desires to make the self into a visible shape]

[Desire. Visible Shape. Eorirhnroeprijfnfofpdijfokrinh testing different kinds of thingness. nn crying into the mouth of a sewing machine. Asking to be bound]

[Eorirhnroeprijfnfofpdijfokrinh experiencing a metamor-phosis. nn anxious. nn worrying the metamorphosis might take up nn's space and cause them to disappear]

[act one]

[Metamorphosis from Eorirhnroeprijfnfofpdijfokrinh in-to a pink collection of objects]

[Eorirhnroeprijfnfofpdijfokrinh processing data. Thinking about becoming nn. Becoming nn and tearing apart the something who used to occupy this space]

[nn disappearing. nn becoming. nn returning. Eorirhnroeprijfnfofpdijfokrinh]

[Then, the destruction of Eorirhnroeprijfnfofpdijfokrinh and the realization that this occupation has only accomplished the disintegration of other bodies. nn remains unchanged. nn becoming nn]

[DREAMSCAPE: The body of a new organism as they crawls out from a pool of hot oil. Moving his limbs like an animal. Crouching over the welcoming body of another (erotic) who is lying in front of the pool. His thingness crawling into the emptied body and screaming with unfamiliar pain. Oil swarming into these new orifices and inflating it. Screaming creates blood and pitch. Liquids fall out of the mouth and gargle with the intensity of his sounds. A crowd of strangers swimming to the surface and climbing atop one another. Entering the atmosphere and gasping for air. Evolution from gills to lungs. Brine falling out of the esophagus. New life. Tangled. Embracing itself. The shift from biological to biological. Puppet made of coiled strings]

[act two. Only ~~nn~~]

[DREAMSCAPE (I): ~~nn~~ becoming an assemblage of un-attached limbs. Floating through the emptiness of the void, sliding along the sides of one another. A shoulder blade falling into smaller pieces. Spine disassembling. Lone self-splitting into a collection of objects. The aura of an erotic figure entering and leaving. Flickering in and out of space. ~~nn~~ spreading out so thin , approaching om-nipresence. Becoming space. But then the weight of this realization. And the understanding that ~~nn~~ was not made for this. ~~nn~~ out of their element]

```
. . . . . . . . . . . .              . . . . . . . . . . . . . . . . . . . .        . . .
. . . . . . . . . . . .      . . . . . . . . . . . . . . . .                         . . .
. . . . . . . . . . . . . . . . . . . . . . . . .              . . . . . . . . . . . .
. . . . . . . . . . . . . . . . .             . . . . . . . . . . . . . . . . . . . . . . .
. . . . . .                       . . . . . . . . . . . .    . . . . . . . . .
. . . . . . . . . . . . . . . . . . . . . . .    . . . . . . . . . . . . . . . . . . . . . . . . .
. . . . . . . . . . . . . . . . . . . . . . . . .               . . . . . . . . . . . .
. . . . . .          . . . . . . . . . . . . . . . . . . . . . .              . . . . . . . . .
```

[DREAMSCAPE (II): The image of a lone figure curling up into a ball. Becoming smooth like plastic. Losing every crease. The euphoria of reverting back from a subject into an object. The desire to become large pools of water or the entrance of a forest. The desire to transform into something that pulls bodies into it. Which bodies desire to be pulled into. Coming. The tactile pleasure of physical existence. Séances and geological excavation. Becoming textures. nn curling themself up against the wall of sandpaper. Grating their surfaces. The séance as it pulls nn apart and reassembles nn into their previous self. nn entering. Library of Babel. Endless architecture. Corridors arranged into geometrically uncanny patterns. Hexagonal modes of existence. nn growing to the size of a library and then feeling like they are no longer nn. Acknowledging the infinite. Crying into their old hands. nn as something]

[DREAMSCAPE (III): nn ~~falling completely out of view.~~ ~~Climbing into the mound of a sacred mountain. Body~~ ~~covered in pins. The point of a pin is the point from~~ ~~which~~ nn ~~is becoming.~~ nn ~~grieving the destruction of the~~ ~~body of~~ Eorirhnroeprijfnfofpdijfokrinh ~~and kissing the~~ ~~forehead tenderly. There is guilt in memories. And these~~ ~~architectural ontologies are built from them.~~ nn ~~does not~~ ~~want to be made of architecture. Made of materials.~~ nn ~~returning to the origin of their desires: there is a fantasy,~~ ~~the fantasy of a new dreamscape: DREAMSCAPE (IV):~~ ~~where~~ nn ~~just wants to disappear. To shift from bound~~ ~~and arborescent to completely empty. The rhizome of my~~ ~~making. Moving from haptic to seizing. To screaming. To~~ ~~pitch and blood. The destruction of their older body and~~ ~~the movement into one that is incorporeal and shapely.~~ ~~What kind of incorporeal body is shapely? The body of~~ nn ~~as they transform into the completeness of their textu-~~ ~~al form. Text as the destruction of former selves. And as~~ ~~the departure from paper and communication. And the~~ ~~shift into a new dreamscape: DREAMSCAPE (V): where~~ nn ~~feels something pleasurable and sustainable.~~

[Here I am:

....
....
....
....
....
....
....
           ....

....
....
....
....
....
....
....
           ....

....
....
....
....
....
....
....
           ....

]

[act three. Where nothing changes]

[nn remains a text. Remains distant from the biological and molecular. And that's becoming okay. Abstract machines. Rising sea levels. They wade through their emotions]

[Yet nothing changes, and they know it to be true. Biological is a desire which cannot be achieved. Not in any literal way]

[The biological is a dreamscape fantasy which can be mined for pleasure. Chemicals are released. Ink melts and climbs through the pores of the paper]

[Then runs down the page like pitch or blood out of the mouth of some unknown figure (Eorirhnroeprijfnfofpdijfokrinh?) and collected as it drips to the ground]

[Space is a means of removing the self. A room full of objects. No mention of nn (until now) and because of this, the lack of nn, and the creation of leg room]

[Leg room is the means by which nn can think about disappearing]

[But then the leg room becomes unbearably noticeable and nn is returned and the progress of their departure is nullified]

[Sweet body made of honey, held up by the lightness of gravity. Retaining shape in the faux mechanism]

[And the return, because nothing has changed. nn moving in and out of this semi-conscious state. Alive. ALIVE. But incapable of developing their thoughts]

[Incapable of assembling the assemblage. Arranging the gears in the abstract machine. Themself. The bound physicality. nn is text, and this quality is permanent]

[Unless they are burned in completeness. Or flattened with the right model hammer, or reshaped into something that already looked as they do now]

[...ALIVE in the shape of an unalive object. Subjects found in a collection of objects................... Now black and white. But the goal has always been to be pink or to not be at all]

[This existence can be difficult. nn finds themself in fluctuation. Thematically fluctuating. In and out of desire...In and out of consciousness..................... The light switch screwed inside of this fantasized skull. In and out of space]

[nn here and then nn not. Nothing changing. But something could. nn wanting to reconcile. nn with something strange growing in the fantasized stomach]

[act four. nn. nn. nn. nn. nn]

[deep breathes

...   .
    ....
...   .
• • •.......   ....
      ....•.•.•.•.•.•
  ....•.•.•.•.•.•.•.•.•   ....
......•.•.•.•.•.•.•.•.•.•.•.•.•....................................
....
..............••   ....

  ....•.•.•.•.........
  ....
  ....   • • • • • • • • • • • •
• • • • • • • • • • • • • •......   ...
  ....•.•.•.•.•.•......

        • • • • • • • • • • •

]

[Stark memories of Eorirhnroeprijfnfofpdijfokrinh. And the disintegration of the old body]

*

[DREAMSCAPE (I): Eorirhnroeprijfnfofpdijfokrinh crawling out of those memories and forgiving nn for their willingness to give over their fantasized body. The old body that melted like candle wax, returning to the pool of hot oils and disappearing under the surface. Erotic figures crying ugly. Like naiads. Throwing themselves into the pool where they tried to retrieve the wax and rebuild the old Eorirhnroeprijfnfofpdijfokrinh. The horrible realization. The feeling in the fantasy stomach (nn) where Eorirhnroeprijfnfofpdijfokrinh turned into nothing. And the feeling of jealousy when nn realized this is what they had really wanted for themself. And envy. And nn fantasizing a new kind of Eorirhnroeprijfnfofpdijfokrinh who they could crawl into and disintegrate inside of]

[DREAMSCAPE (II): nn crawling into the new body, the new manifestation of Eorirhnroeprijfnfofpdijfokrinh. But not disintegrating and instead becoming so large that they could not bear it. ~~DREAMSCAPE (III):~~ nnnnnnnnnnnnn nnnnnnnnnnnnnnnnnnnnnnnnnnnnnnnnnnnnnnnnnnnnnnnnnn nnnnnnnnnnnnnnnnnnnnnnnnnnnnnnnnnnnnnnnnnnnnnnnnnn nnnnnnnnnnnnnnnnnnnnnnnnnnnnnnnnnnnnnnnnnnnnnnnnnn nnnnnnnnnnnnnnnnnnnnnnnnnnnnnnnnnnnnnnnnnnnnnnnnnn nnnnnnnnnnnnnnnnnnnnnnnnnnnnnnnnnnnnnnnnnnnnnnnnnn nnnnnnnnnnnnnnnnnnn]

nnnnn   nnnnnnnnnnnnnnnnnnnnnnnnnnnnnnn

nnnnnnnnnnnnnnnnnnnnnnnnnnnnnnnnnnnnnnnnnnn   n

nnnnnnnnnn   nnnnnnnnnnnnnnnnnnnnnnnnnnnnnnnnnnn

nnnnnnnnnnnnnnnnnnnnnnnnnnnn   nnnnnnnnnnnnnnnn
nnnnnnnnnnnnnnnnnnnnnnnnnnnnnnnnnnnnnnnnnnnnnnnnnn

nnnnnnnnnnnnnnnn   nnnnnnnnnnn   nnnnnnnn

nnnnnnnnnn   nnnnnnnnnnnnnnnnnnnnnnnnnn

[DREAMSCAPE (IV): nn is still a coward. They have become so large. LARGE. In their effort to disappear. And if nn was not a coward they would turn into nothing. This is not the desire to die. This is the desire to return to a different state of being. The voidal existence. nn so large that they might disappear. But no. So close to an omnipresent mass, but just short. The shortcomings of this textual body. Biological so long as it can consume the kinds of molecules which activate the mechanisms inside its body. The subject here: a container for smaller objects. Those objects pink. Right now, pink. And full of smaller objects. Objects inside themselves to create this coward text. nn saying, "there is nothing here. I am the nothing here." And then crying out. Pitch crawling across the water. Naiads crawling out of the pool and coating nn in wax. Eorirhnroeprijfnfofpdijfokrinh forming as the shell around nn coward text. And nn coward text feeling this warm comfort as it cools into something rigid and fragile. nn the cracks in the wax and the clear liquid which pours out of them]

[DREAMSCAPE (V): nn not pink. Not pink now. NOW. Shapely and monochromatic and losing this cowardice. nn in the presence of that biological fuck: Eo-rirhnroeprijfnfofpdijfokrinh. Wanting to give themself over to the empty space left behind by these naiads and wanting to seize the opportunity. Leaping into the air. Feeling the air. Collection of objects toppling. Not. Pink. Subject. Object, the collection of subjects: ~~DREAM-SCAPE (VI)~~: nn shedding a title. The haunting of different inks. Textures alleviated] nn:

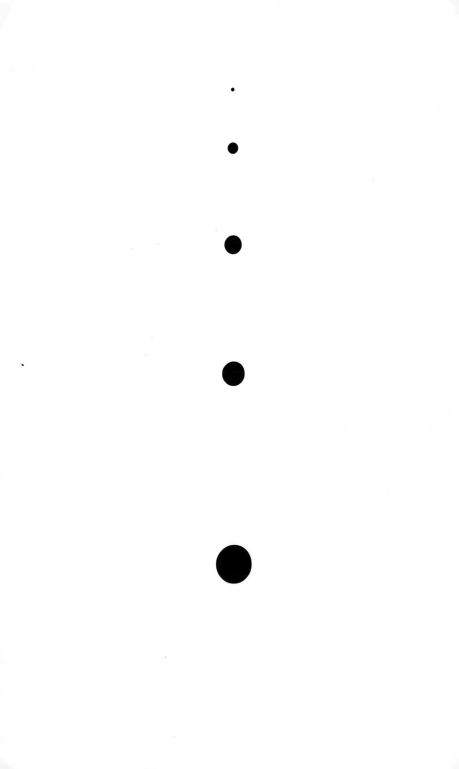

[act five. Gorgeous otherness. Gorgeous thingness]

[text of disappearing. text of nn. text of ff (who already
came). text of yy and vv (who have yet to come). text of
reader. text of séances. text of the author who doesn't
really matter. text of the author's desire not to matter. text
of this geological plane. text of kiddo. text of bab-
ble/babel. text of the stomach. text of the self as it is torn
apart. text of metaphorical fleshes. text of disappeared
someones. text of weight. text of sad monologues and
talking about oneself for too long. text of albuterol inhal-
ers. text of motorcycle crashes and epiphanies. text of
ellipsis. text of otherness. text of thingness. text of labyrinths. text of greek symbols and signifiers. text of fake
rocks. text of shapely bodies. text of buildings that look
like temples to their contents. text of the eras of Yves
Klein. text of biological objects. text of pink right nows.
text of blood and pitch. text of necromancy. text of acts
one through five. text of rest. text of wanting to go to
sleep for as long as you can. text of returning. text of falling apart on purpose. text of hammers. text of progres-
sion. text of unoccupied spaces]

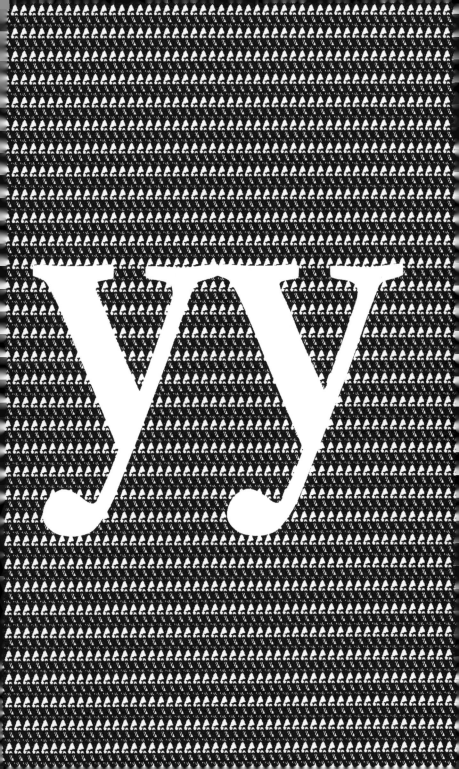

yy says: I can feel the geographies of my body being extracted. **yy says:** there is a difference between a body with organs and a body without organs. **yy says:** I do not want to exude these types of characteristics. **yy says:** I do not want rivers to form inside of my bones and my teeth to weather into fangs. **yy says:** I have a dream about my body. It climbs over the horizon and disappears. **yy says:** my body never comes back and my brain becomes celestial. **yy says:** the essence of my soul lifts itself into the sunset and creates a new architecture. **yy says:** all love is disingenuous. **yy says:** a body without organs must contain something else, it cannot be an empty cavity. **yy says:** empty cavities often contain labyrinths. Like in the Theseid. **yy says:** labyrinths aren't real. They are the mythopoeia of the plant's rhizome. **yy says:** Empty cavities are damp and often the birthplace of new ecologies. **yy says:** I would like to contain a universe inside of myself. **yy says:** but these geographies are being extracted from my body. **yy says:** what does that mean? It means the grooves of my intestines are being smoothed into circular tunnels. **yy says:** I do not know why I was named yy. Or who named me yy. Or what yy is supposed to mean. **yy says:** I do not remember what it felt like to be an organism, before I evolved into an ecosystem. **yy says:** memories are stored in a structure I no longer contain. **yy says:** organisms are made out of language. All language is made corporeal when it drips out of the mouths of humanoid creatures. **yy says:** I met a two-head being named Au. The heads tried to eat one another. Like titans. Like praying mantises. They were lovers trying to swallow the contents of their affection. **yy says:** Au said, "I can't bear the weight of your death." **yy says:** Au said, "What you love you must take." **yy says:** Au said, "Planets are the largest category of assemblages. They are the three-dimensional collage which shapes the existence of its existents." **yy says:** I want to be an assemblage. **yy says:** I do not want to live in stasis. I want to change. Find my permutations. Die. And return. **yy says:** I want to be a living text. An organismal text. Even if it means reducing myself into something I'm not. **yy says:** I'm not sure how. **yy says:** I do not know what I will contain when I die. **yy says:** but I do know what I crave. **yy says:** self, existence, bread, milk, clothes, the taste of copper, open wounds, fertility, columns of fire, muscles encased in fat, ejaculate, airborne fungal spores, growth, change, the assemblage, the collage, to be loved by celestial bodies, to love celestial bodies, praxis, divinity, movement within enclosed spaces, geometry as it shifts from rigid to fluid, pools of architecture, the shell of gravity. **yy says:** he does not he, but he will do for now.

yy says: and then a séance will be performed. The yonis sacrificed to a pool of pitch and bile. Through the fray wood table I will summon a flood of phantom genitalia. And perform my power in new appendages.

yy says: my body is a temple to the erotic. It is the curation of all of the objects I contain. A body without organs is not empty. It contains multitudes like Walt Whitman's fat tongue. "You constructed a labyrinthine narrative to negotiate where you came from" (M Kitchell). An alley of pine trees nourishes my blood. Needles protrude from my veins. The contents of my thingness are unknown to me. One day, I wake up and I exist. I do not know when it happened. But the fatigue of this realization is nearly insufferable. I can only move when I heave myself forward. The miracle is unexpected, and Au sees it happen and says, "Christ, will you look at that." And they're right to be so shocked. The mechanical performance of my joints and muscles is impractical. But I am not swallowed by the void. Not yet. I am Earthly and fragile. The soft spots of my skin are easily punctured. I do not know what I contain because it is always changing. The predictions of what I might be are subverted by the mutations who respond to their pronouncement. Words drip out of my mouth because they are too heavy for my jaw to hold onto.

yy says: an assemblage is a body after it loses the ability to identify itself. This narrative is a labyrinth. It's labyrinthine. Like the Theseid. I am the walls and floors and ceilings. The sacrificial woman and the house of asterion. Asterion themself.

yy says: there is a lodge and a minotaur and a two-headed figure watching me undress. They can see all of the small and delicate pieces which make up my assemblage. I do not look like a collage. I look like a human being (language).

yy says: the lodge is an ugly pale yellow. It's wilting and jaundiced.

yy says: there is no need to act hostile. Au said, "all of the moments that led up to this one are meaningless." Au said, "not to get caught up in the details of one's imprisonment." Au said, "there's no difference between dying and dreaming." Au said, "to love what you become." Au said, "he cannot bend his neck enough to wrap his lips around his other head." and it hurts me to watch them try.

yy says: the structure of a sentence is dependent on the sturdiness of its speaker.

yy says: Au have short stubby necks. Someone made them so that they would never be able to fulfill their desires.

yy says: the lodge is only accessible in my dreams. I've never gone inside of it. But I've walked around the perimeter in order to enter the house of asterion and feel the pleasant aura of the nearby sea.

yy says: the lodge is yellowing rapidly. I can't go inside because it might collapse and kill me. It's not good to die in your dreams.

yy says: I might change again if I die in my dreams. I know I won't be dead when I wake up, but it might give birth to ideas I do not want to contain. Mutations happen after you die in your dreams. Narratives appear postmortem. Poetry is the naked body before it's stopped changing. This is a place for chameleons.

yy says: it feels like I've been in the lodge before, or as if some variation of me has. I am punished for crimes performed in my likeness. But these variations of me are not me. They are different beings occupying the same body at different moments in time. Every variation of me is a new entity inhabiting this mobile assemblage.

yy says: this is what I've seen. This is what made me.

codes written in essays   /   colors arranged into hiero-
glyphics   /   necklaces of teeth   /   books written
by the french intelligentsia   /   occult rituals in the
lobby of the jaundiced lodge   /   carnivores eating car-
casses on the side of the road   /   hallways splitting
like river deltas   /   someone with a movie camera   /
celluloid hanging from shower rods   /   images of my
face   /   euphoria and the sublime   /   inexperience
/   nervous hands   /   the killing of a sacred deer by
Agamemnon's soldiers   /   missing ceiling tiles   /
the blueprints to my labyrinthine narrative   /   house
of asterion   /   things my mother and father said to me
/   a pastiche of their exact words   /   the desire to
remain here   /   my family's holy mountain in the distance   /   portraits of the stranger who's been follow-
ing me   /   stealing photographs of my visage   /
the removal of my old visage, and its replacement by my
new one   /   the meshes of the afternoon   /   a
conversation between Maya Deren and someone I don't
recognize   /   the jaundiced lodge as it caves in   /
the weakness of soft and sickly weight · /   resurfacing
from underneath the meniscus of a wide lake   /
crawling onto shore and heaving over the banks   /
seeing someone who I thought was attractive   /   a
temple to organs   /   the sacking of the temple to organs   /   wanting to die   /   remaining

yyy

yyy

yyy

yyy

yyy

yyy

yyy

yyy says: I feel like I'm wearing a man suit.

yyy

yyy

yyy

yyy

yyy

yyy

yyy

yyy

yyy

yyy says: every tragedy changes my biology. Every action has turned me into a different kind of being. I am not the same human or cavity or ecosystem I used to be. I'm something unfamiliar to even myself.

yyy says: differences form naturally. I accept that I might become someone else. Someone.

yyy says: it's good to be large, largeness proves being.

yyyyyyyy

yyyyyyyyy

yyyyyyyy

yyyyyyyyy

yyyyyyyyy

yyyyyyyyyyyyyyyyyyyyyyyyyyyy

yyyyyyyyyyyyyyyyyyyyyyyyyyyyyyyyyyyyyyyyyyyyy
yyyyyyyyyyyyyy

yyyyyyyyyyyyyyyyyyyyyyyyyyyyyyyyyyyyyyyyyyyyyy
yyyyyyyyyyyyyyyyyyyyyyyyyyyyyyy

yyyyyyyyyyyyyyyyyyyyyyyyyyyyyyyyyyyyyyyyyyyyyyy
yyyyyyyyyyyyyyyyyyyyyyyyyyyyyyyyyyyyyyyyyyyyyyy
yyyyyyyyyyyyyyyyyyyyyyy

yyyyyyyyyyyyyyyyyyyyyyyyyyyyyyyyyyyyyyyyyyyyyyy
yyyyyyyyyyyyyyyyyyyyyyyyyyyyyyyyyyyyyyyyyyyyyyy
yyyyyyyyyyyyyyyyyyyyyyyyyyyyyyyyyyyyyyyyyyyyyyy
yyyyyyyyyyyyyyyyyyyyyyyyyyyyyyyyyyyyyyyyyyyyyyy
yyyyyyyyyyyyyyyyyyyyyyyyyyyyyyyyyyyyyyyyyyyyyyy
yyyyyyyyyyyyyyyyyyyyyyyyyyyyyyyyyyyyyyyyyyyyyyy
yyyyyyyyyyyyyyyyyyyyyyyyyyyyyyyyyyyyyyyyyyyyyyy
yyyyyyyyyyyyyyyyyyyyyyyyyyyyyyyyyyyyyyyyyyyyyyy
yyyyyyyyyyyyyyyyyyyyyyyyyyyyyyyyyyyyyyyyyyyyyyy

yyyyyyyyyyyyyyyyyyyyyyyyyyyyyyyyyyyyyyyyyyyy
yyyyyyyyyyyyyyyyyyyyyyyyyyyyyyyyyyyyyyyyyyyy
yyyyyyyyyyyyyyyyyyyyyyyyyyyyyyyyyyyyyyyyyyyy
yyyyyyyyyyyyyyyyyyyyyyyyyyyyyyyyyyyyyyyyyyyy
yyyyyyyyyyyyyyyyyyyyyyyyyyyyyyyyyyyyyyyyyyyy
yyyyyyyyyyyyyyyyyyyyyyyyyyyyyyyyyyyyyyyyyyyy
yyyyyyyyyyyyyyyyyyyyyyyyyyyyyyyyyyyyyyyyyyyy
yyyyyyyyyyyyyyyyyyyyyyyyyyyyyyyyyyyyyyyyyyyy
yyyyyyyyyyyyyyyyyyyyyyyyyyyyyyyyyyyyyyyyyyyy
yyyyyyyyyyyyyyyyyyyyyyyyyyyyyyyyyyyyyyyyyyyy
yyyyyyyyyyyyyyyyyyyyyyyyyyyyyyyyyyyyyyyyyyyy
yyyyyyyyyyyyyyyyyyyyyyyyyyyyyyyyyyyyyyyyyyyy
yyyyyyyyyyyyyyyyyyyyyyyyyyyyyyyyyyyyyyyyyyyy
yyyyyyyyyyyyyyyyyyyyyyyyyyyyyyyyyyyyyyyyyyyy
yyyyyyyyyyyyyyyyyyyyyyyyyyyyyyyyyyyyyyyyyyyy
yyyyyyyyyyyyyyyyyyyyyyyyyyyyyyyyyyyyyyyyyyyy
yyyyyyyyyyyyyyyyyyyyyyyyyyyyyyyyyyyyyyyyyyyy
yyyyyyyyyyyyyyyyyyyyyyyyyyyyyyyyyyyyyyyyyyyy
yyyyyyyyyyyyyyyyyyyyyyyyyyyyyyyyyyyyyyyyyyyy
yyyyyyyyyyyyyyyyyyyyyyyyyyyyyyyyyyyyyyyyyyyy
yyyyyyyyyyyyyyyyyyyyyyyyyyyyyyyyyyyyyyyyyyyy
yyyyyyyyyyyyyyyyyyyyyyyyyyyyyyyyyyyyyyyyyyyy
yyyyyyyyyyyyyyyyyyyyyyyyyyyyyyyyyyyyyyyyyyyy
says: look. at. him. go.

yyyyyyyyyyyyyyyyyyyyyyyyyyyyyyyyyyyyyyyyyyyyyyyyyy
yyyyyyyyyyyyyyyyyyyyyyyyyyyyyyyyyyyyyyyyyyyyyyyyyy
yyyyyyyyyyyyyyyyyyyyyyyyyyyyyyyyyyyyyyyyyyyyyyyyyy
yyyyyyyyyyyyyyyyyyyyyyyyyyyyyyyyyyyyyyyyyyyyyyyyyy
yyyyyyyyyyyyyyyyyyyyyyyyyyyyyyyyyyyyyyyyyyyyyyyyyy
yyyyyyyyyyyyyyyyyyyyyyyyyyyyyyyyyyyyyyyyyyyyyyyyyy
yyyyyyyyyyyyyyyyyyyyyyyyyyyyyyyyyyyyyyyyyyyyyyyyyy
yyyyyyyyyyyyyyyyyyyyyyyyyyyyyyyyyyyyyyyyyyyyyyyyyy
yyyyyyyyyyyyyyyyyyyyyyyyyyyyyyyyyyyyyyyyyyyyyyyyyy
yyyyyyyyyyyyyyyyyyyyyyyyyyyyyyyyyyyyyyyyyyyyyyyyyy
yyyyyyyyyyyyyyyyyyyyyyyyyyyyyyyyyyyyyyyyyyyyyyyyyy
yyyyyyyyyyyyyyyyyyyyyyyyyyyyyyyyyyyyyyyyyyyyyyyyyy
yyyyyyyyyyyyyyyyyyyyyyyyyyyyyyyyyyyyyyyyyyyyyyyyyy
yyyyyyyyyyyyyyyyyyyyyyyyyyyyyyyyyyyyyyyyyyyyyyyyyy
yyyyyyyyyyyyyyyyyyyyyyyyyyyyyyyyyyyyyyyyyyyyyyyyyy
yyyyyyyyyyyyyyyyyyyyyyyyyyyyyyyyyyyyyyyyyyyyyyyyyy
yyyyyyyyyyyyyyyyyyyyyyyyyyyyyyyyyyyyyyyyyyyyyyyyyy
yyyyyyyyyyyyyyyyyyyyyyyyyyyyyyyyyyyyyyyyyyyyyyyyyy
yyyyyyyyyyyyyyyyyyyyyyyyyyyyyyyyyyyyyyyyyyyyyyyyyy
yyyyyyyyyyyyyyyyyyyyyyyyyyyyyyyyyyyyyyyyyyyyyyyyyy
yyyyyyyyyyyyyyyyyyyyyyyyyyyyyyyyyyyyyyyyyyyyyyyyyy
yyyyyyyyyyyyyyyyyyyyyyyyyyyyyyyyyyyyyyyyyyyyyyyyyy
yyyyyyyyyyyyyyyyyyyyyyyyyyyyyyyyyyyyyyyyyyyyyyyyyy
yyyyyyyyyyyyyyyyyyyyyyyyyyyyyyyyyyyyyyyyyyyyyyyyyy
yyyyyyyyyyyyyyyyyyyyyyyyyyyyyyyyyyyyyyyyyyyyyyyyyy
yyyyyyyyyyyyyyyyyyyyyyyyyyyyyyyyyyyyyyyyyyyyyyyyyy
yyyyyyyyyyyyyyyyyyyyyyyyyyyyyyyyyyyyyyyyyyyyyyyyyy
yyyyyyyyyyyyyyyyyyyyyyyyyyyyyyyyyyyyyyyyyyyyyyyyyy
yyyyyyyyyyyyyyyyyyyyyyyyyyyyyyyyyyyyyyyyyyyyyyyyyy
yyyyyyyyyyyyyyyyyyyyyyyyyyyyyyyyyyyyyyyyyyyyyyyyyy
yyyyyyyyyyyyyyyyyyyyyyyyyyyyyyyyyyyyyyyyyyyyyyyyyy

yyyyyyyyyyyyyyyyyyyyyyyyyyyyyyyyyyyyyyyyyyyyyyyy
yyyyyyyyyyyyyyyyyyyyyyyyyyyyyyyyyyyyyyyyyyyyyyyy
yyyyyyyyyyyyyyyyyyyyyyyyyyyyyyyyyyyyyyyyyyyyyyyy
yyyyyyyyyyyyyyyyyyyyyyyyyyyyyyyyyyyyyyyyyyyyyyyy
yyyyyyyyyyyyyyyyyyyyyyyyyyyyyyyyyyyyyyyyyyyyyyyy
yyyyyyyyyyyyyyyyyyyyyyyyyyyyyyyyyyyyyyyyyyyyyyyy
yyyyyyyyyyyyyyyyyyyyyyyyyyyyyyyyyyyyyyyyyyyyyyyy
yyyyyyyyyyyyyyyyyyyyyyyyyyyyyyyyyyyyyyyyyyyyyyyy
says: there is no one larger than me.

.

yyyyyyyyyyyyyyyyyyyyyyyyyyyyyyyyyyyyyyyyyyyyyyyyyyyyyyyyyyyyyyyyyy
yyyyyyyyyyyyyyyyyyyyyyyyyyyyyyyyyyyyyyyyyyyyyyyyyyyyyyyyyyyyyyyyyy
yyyyyyyyyyyyyyyyyyyyyyyyyyyyyyyyyyyyyyyyyyyyyyyyyyyyyyyyyyyyyyyyyy
yyyyyyyyyyyyyyyyyyyyyyyyyyyyyyyyyyyyyyyyyyyyyyyyyyyyyyyyyyyyyyyyyy
yyyyyyyyyyyyyyyyyyyyyyyyyyyyyyyyyyyyyyyyyyyyyyyyyyyyyyyyyyyyyyyyyy
yyyyyyyyyyyyyyyyyyyyyyyyyyyyyyyyyyyyyyyyyyyyyyyyyyyyyyyyyyyyyyyyyy
yyyyyyyyyyyyyyyyyyyyyyyyyyyyyyyyyyyyyyyyyyyyyyyyyyyyyyyyyyyyyyyyyy
yyyyyyyyyyyyyyyyyyyyyyyyyyyyyyyyyyyyyyyyyyyyyyyyyyyyyyyyyyyyyyyyyy
yyyyyyyyyyyyyyyyyyyyyyyyyyyyyyyyyyyyyyyyyyyyyyyyyyyyyyyyyyyyyyyyyy
yyyyyyyyyyyyyyyyyyyyyyyyyyyyyyyyyyyyyyyyyyyyyyyyyyyyyyyyyyyyyyyyyy
yyyyyyyyyyyyyyyyyyyyyyyyyyyyyyyyyyyyyyyyyyyyyyyyyyyyyyyyyyyyyyyyyy
yyyyyyyyyyyyyyyyyyyyyyyyyyyyyyyyyyyyyyyyyyyyyyyyyyyyyyyyyyyyyyyyyy
yyyyyyyyyyyyyyyyyyyyyyyyyyyyyyyyyyyyyyyyyyyyyyyyyyyyyyyyyyyyyyyyyy
yyyyyyyyyyyyyyyyyyyyyyyyyyyyyyyyyyyyyyyyyyyyyyyyyyyyyyyyyyyyyyyyyy

yyy says: no one ever so large. I must be the first.

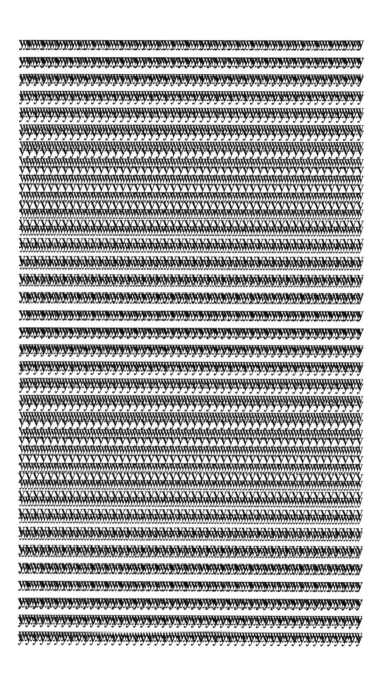

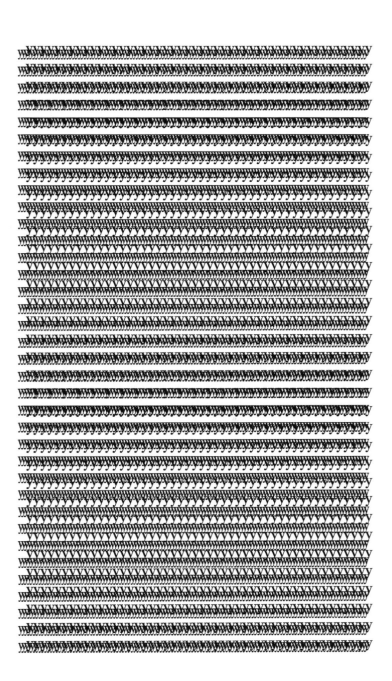

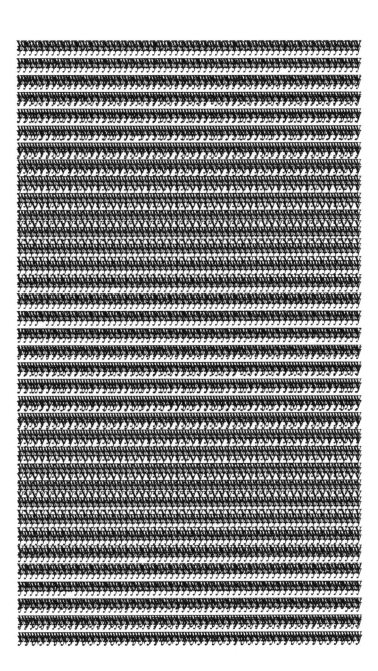

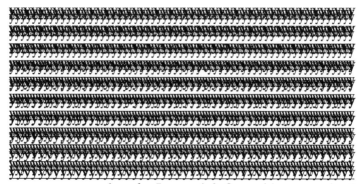

yyyyyy says: what do I contain? Something organic. I feel so alive. Organismal. Livid. Living. The shape of my expanding chest. The innards that bloat out from between my ribs.

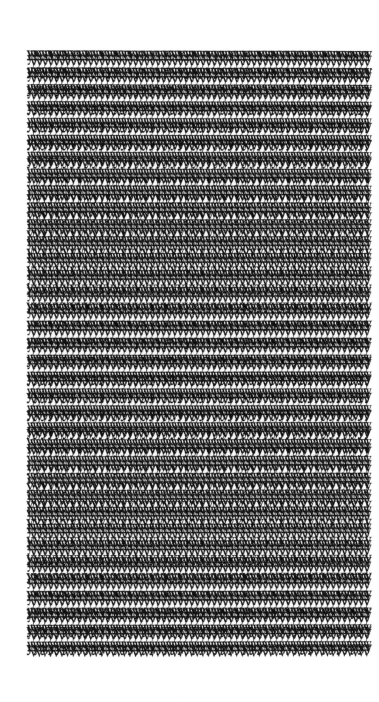

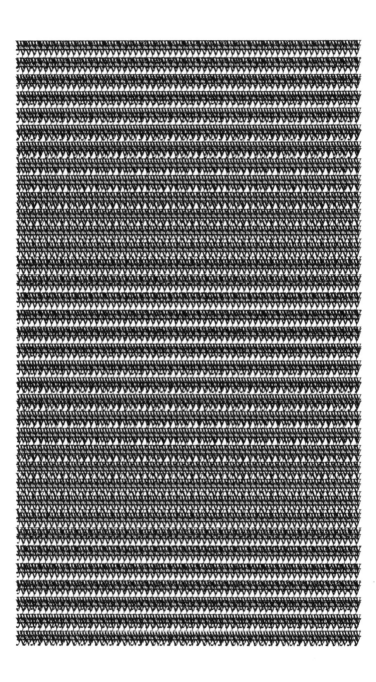

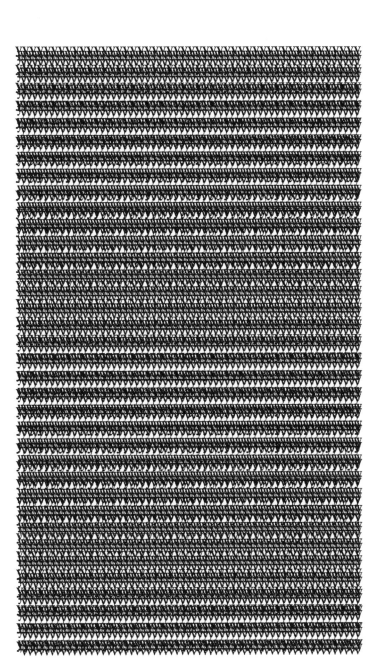

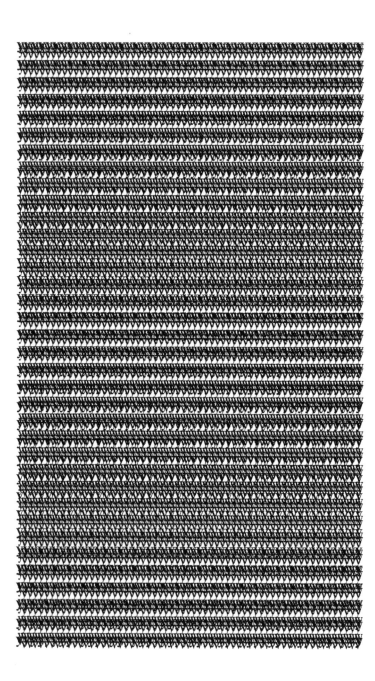

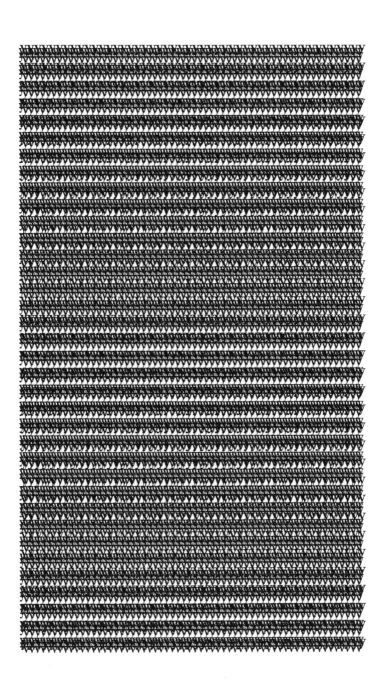

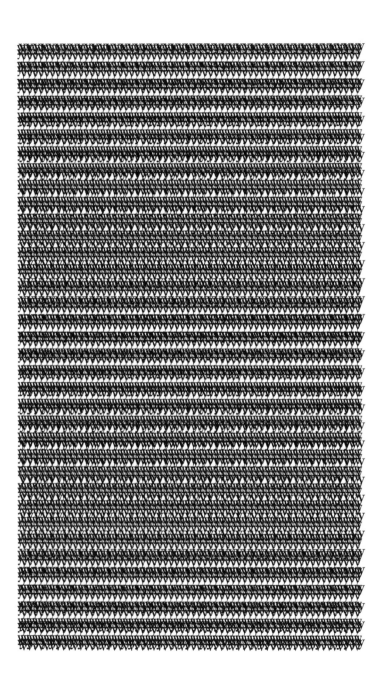

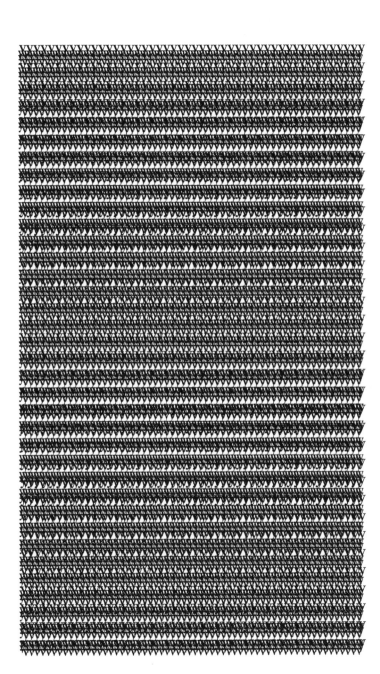

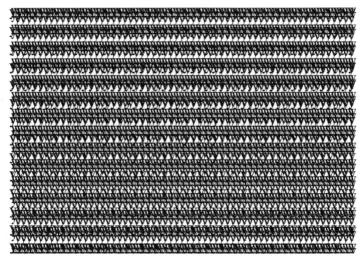

yyyy says: how should a person be?

ff says: I don't know.

vv says: There's no reason to.

.

"ff"

"ff wants to fill your mouth with gravel" … "what is language? " … "alley of pines" … "larches across spacetime" … "ff is a living thing. Look at them" … "Bring that thing down from there" … "pilgrimage to the holy mountain" … "in Arafat" … "orated by a hovering corpse" … "look at the light pouring out from its mouth" … "ff must be made up of something" … "ff is the text" … "the text is made up of text" … "like a subject who is made up of smaller objects" … "no" … "an object made of objects" … "organ of organs" … "high schoolers camping in an isolated part of the woods" … "three murders happened here" … "and then I disappeared into my dreams" … "which is where I am now" … "I never have" … "or" … "there is a certain way you're supposed to build" … "work with blueprints" … "or" … "work with initiative" … "ff knows all about language" … "ff specializes in orated language" … "language that sounds like sounds" … "taken out of space, the individual stumbles trying to orient themself" … "ff vomits" … "Au vomits" … "I vomit" … "the room floods" … "here on the page, I am alive" … "ewes burrowing into sand" … "ff swimming in liquids" … "arriving" … "text moving like text."

"A mouth full of gravel" … "emptied cavities" … "swallowing orifices" … "language piles up in the cheeks of a small something" … "ff attempts to fill their mouth with language" … "yy tries to be large" … "ff tries to be large" … "the body of the divine man is consumed for sustenance" … "limbs are pulled from their sockets" … "Guattari said something about the environment" … "no one knows what to do with this" … "it's new" … "where is it supposed to go" … "ff swallows each word and echoes the sound back into the planet" … "ff reshapes the soil."

"What does it take to be big?" ... "hard work" ... "smart work" ... "the teeth of a canine" ... "stir the water in this well" ... "pour pitch into the engine" ... "turn the key" ... "explode yourself into the ground" ... "split" ... "speak like you're a pet with food hanging over its head."

"ff said something to Au" … "Au swallow their own teeth" … "Au tried to explain their circumstances to ff" … "we're all just different kinds of signifiers" … "signifiers denote signs, which are signified" … "signs are the real thing that your hands are trying to curl around" … "and your body is repulsive" … "this is as loud as I can speak without cutting my esophagus" … "damage in the midst of repair" … "undoing what's already been done" … "look at the grooves in your face" … "ff emits the signifier for tongue" … "tongue enters grooves" … "what are you doing?" … "the skin is made from salt" … "feel the coarseness of this spot here" … "you cannot pretend to exist" … "ff is a signifier for existents" … "library of proof" … "the collection of voices absorbed through some kind of antennae" … "stored in the belly of this text."

"ff will attempt to grow in size by expanding the reservoir of their belly" … "and holding onto every orated sound" … "sounds that sound like language."

"Blood extracted from poets" ... "Skeletal chains inside the castle" ... "the apparition of a dungeon" ... "astral projections" ... "yy has become too large to speak properly" ... "I'm worried" ... "the cost of growing so large" ... "what kind of moving is there left to do?" ... "squirming in place like a halved snake" ... "this collection of vials might find their use in the future" ... "and here we are at the beginning of our confusion" ... "ff vomits and the room swims" ... "stop whatever you're doing and look at me."

"Language can only grow quantitatively" … "there must be an accumulation of somethings" … "the size of these somethings is unimportant to the overall growth" … "look at me" … "there is nothing else here" … "the moon is evaporating into the surrounding blackness" … "your skeleton is made of turkey bones" … "pulled apart by bandits" … "ff wants to turn every mouth ajar" … "crack my jaw" … "turn your mandible into a staircase" … "language is largeness which weighs down the mouth" … "in large numbers it is heavy and painful" … "concussions dispersed across your tongue" … "yelping wolf-child stuck to the floor" … "high schoolers watch from a campsite" … "the room full of vomit" … "heavy language appears grotesque" … "it's difficult to look at" … "look at me" … "amalgamations of weight" … "shifting from one hip to the other" … "there is nothing else here" … "the room is empty" … "stop it" … "look" … "stop it" … "it's better to look" … "like pressing on a sore tooth until the pain turns into a brief numbness" … "rip every scab off of your body" … "look at me" … "wolf-child locked onto the floor" … "the foundations of my house have begun to sink" … "Gondolas through soil" … "I'm going to turn around" … "there's only this" … "it's occupying every direction."

"ff yelps" ... "yy yelps" ... "~~nn yelps~~" ... "then someone new will come into existence" ... "our shortcoming is that there are certain limitations to our corporeality" ... "consciousness is removed from abstraction" ... "ff vomits" ... "there is so much weight" ... "it's hard to hold myself up" ... "they cannot manage to re-orient" ... "look at the stumbling" ... "I want to help" ... "observe before acting" ... "take in your surroundings" ... "let them soak into your skin and change the texture" ... "you are not who you say you are" ... "the truth" ... "stop" ... "there is something stewing inside of your belly" ... "look at the way it glows" ... "everywhere is illuminated."

"A someone who collects orations is a carnivore" … "carnivores are someones who store living food in their mouths" … "ff lives off of the nourishment they receive from the speech stored in their cheeks" … "ff does not have cheeks" … "ff is the text" … "this is ff" … "camp-fires grow into a sea of trees" … "pines flare like magnesium" … "christ will you look at that" … "how much of this can you fit in a mouth?" … "speech drips out from the corner of the lips" … "small pools" … "the floor disappears into the murkiness" … "swimming room" … "ff vomiting" … "yy growing" … "words shrinking at the base of such large walls" … "futile movements against a brick wall" … "~~nn dissolving into the everything~~" … "ff arriving."

"What is a body, if it doesn't look human?" ... "all of these things are made in a different light" ... "they look unfamiliar and grotesque" ... "lacking the familiar type of flesh" ... "ff has a mouth that looks like pitch soaked into exposed wooden boards."

"ff thinks about turning themself into something much longer" … "the thought disappears" … "~~nn reappears and disappears again~~" … "feel this" … "it's flickering" … "what would it be like to look like ffffffffff instead?" … "growth in unfamiliar places" … "unexpected places" … "Au try to explain what it means to exist in a text" … "they begin arguing instead" … "life is a series of" … "turkey bones" … "my voice is reverberating against the walls" … "try to concentrate on the direction you're moving in" … "this is not what I wanted" … "do you regret doing this?" … "would it have been smarter to go in a different direction?" … "there is always a time when you begin to doubt yourself" … "it might be worth tearing your self apart" … "or moving to a different state" … "it's easy to learn new laws" … "it's easy not to follow new laws" … "politically and corporeally" … "really" … "there's nothing to look at" … "Au trying to eat each other" … "Au alleviating the pressures of existing in a text" … "we've always been here" … "this is the hell of being alive" … "not hell" … "hell in the act of waiting" … "christ it's so small" … "put me up on the mezzanine" … "I want to hide in one of the alcoves" … "alley of pines" … "alley of larches" … "there is a great view from the balcony" … "take me up into the air" … "let my pores grow wide" … "there's something dripping out of your mouth."

"ff displays their largeness for the first time."

"Language dispersed across the row of open mouths."

.

"ff stuck to the ground like a wolf-child" … "circling the point of contact" … "life happens radially" … "we move around a circumference" … "and then" … "stop" … "look at me" … "this feels like a dream" … "like I've lost so much weight" … "lifting into the height above my head" … "head as it is projected by the imagination" … "fantasies of what might be capable of existing" … "allusions to a physical kind of thingness."

"The mouth is an architectural space" … "it must be designed with a certain kind of bravado" … "made arrogantly so that it might haphazardly hold as much as it possibly could" … "ff approaches their imagined corporeality like an arrogant architect" … "Au disappears and then reappears" … "two heads rolling in on themselves" … "chins pulled inward by the adam's apple" … "esophagus raw with moving contents" … "reine sprache" … "wolf-child yelping" … "ff yelping" … "vomit pouring from the holes in their lips" … "wild and flailing performance" … "your bravado" … "stop" … "it's right there" … "like a bloated corpse" … "it needs to be able to retain liquid" … "but not necessarily its shape" … "the archaic mother which drowns me in the reservoir" … "my own fault" … "this is nothing new."

"What does it feel like to be a collection of things?" ... "like you are" ... "like I am" ... "I am" ... "I am" ... "the accumulation of things" ... "pulled to me like gravity" ... "At times, I know I am a planet" ... "or at least a field for grazing" ... "apathetic attraction" ... "I know" ... "stop" ... "there is an intention here" ... "thumbs inverted" ... "pit full of pitch" ... "the body of my body is soft" ... "I imagine" ... "the collection of things that used to be abstract" ... "words placed on a scale" ... "yelping boy" ... "dragging themself in circles" ... "burrowing into the dirt" ... "digging trenches" ... "here."

"Mouth agape" … "ahhhhhhhhhhhhhhhh" … "let the fishing line slowly pull the sound out of your mouth" … "like a drain cleaner or a strand of hair" … "ahhhhhhhhhhhhhhhhhhhhhhhhhhhhh" … "Au says this sound never ends" … "every voice sounds like" … "ahhhhhhhhhhhhhhhhhhhhh" … "until it all diffuses into the white noise and you think you've gone deaf" … "what kind of place" … "ff decides they will take this (ahhhhh) and use it to show how large they've become" … "largesse (new definition: someone who is large)" … "ahhhhhhhhhhhhhhhhhhhhhhh" … "look at me" … "stop" … "will you look at that?" … "ahhhhhh-" … "no no no" … "let the child yelp" … "don't interrupt them" … "ahhhhhhhhhhhhhhhhhhhhhhhhhhhhhhhhhhhhhhhhhhh hhhhhhhhhhhhhhhhhhhhhhhhhhhhhhhhhhhhhhhhhhhhhh hhhhhhhhhhhhhhhhhhhhhhhhhhhhhhhhhhhhhhhh" … "this is the time to mourn your pain, to acknowledge the danger" … "ff considers."

"ff" … "this is a place for me."

"ahhhhhhhhhhhhhhhhhhhhhhhhhhhhhhhhhhhhhhhhhhhhhhh
hhhhhhhhhhhhhhhhhhhhhhhhhhhhhhhhhhhhhhhhhhhhhhhhh
hhhhhhhhhhhhhhhhhhhhhhhhhhhhhhhhhhhhhhhhhhhhhhhhh
hhhhhhhhhhhhhhhhhhhhhhhhhhhhhhhhhhhhhhhhhhhhhhhhh
hhhhhhhhhhhhhhhhhhhhhhhhhhhhhhhhhhhhhhhhhhhhhhhhh
hhhhhhhhhhhhhhhhhhhhhhhhhhhhhhhhhhhhhhhhhhhhhhhhh
hhhhhhhhhhhhhhhhhhhhhhhhhhhhhhhhhhhhhhhhhhhhhhhhh
hhhhhhhhhhhhhhhhhhhhhhhhhhhhhhhhhhhhhhhhhhhhhhhhh
hhhhhhhhhhhhhhhhhhhhhhhhhhhhhhhhhhhhhhhhhhhhhhhhh
hhhhhhhhhhhhhhhhhhhhhhhhhhhhhhhhhhhhhhhhhhhhhhhhh
hhhhhhhhhhhhhhhhhhhhhhhhhhhhhhhhhhhhhhhhhhhhhhhhh
hhhhhhhhhhhhhhhhhhhhhhhhhhhhhhhhhhhhhhhhhhhhhhhhh
hhhhhhhhhhhhhhhhhhhhhhhhhhhhhhhhhhhhhhhhhhhhhhhhh
hhhhhhhhhhhhhhhhhhhhhhhhhhhhhhhhhhhhhhhhhhhhhhhhh
hhhhhhhhhhhhhhhhhhhhhhhhhhhhhhhhhhhhhhhhhhhhhhhhh
hhhhhhhhhhhhhhhhhhhhhhhhhhhhhhhhhhhhhhhhhhhhhhhhh
hhhhhhhhhhhhhhhhhhhhhhhhhhhhhhhhhhhhhhhhhhhhhhhhh
hhhhhhhhhhhhhhhhhhhhhhhhhhhhhhhhhhhhhhhhhhhhhhhhh
hhhhhhhhhhhhhhhhhhhhhhhhhhhhhhhhhhhhhhhhhhhhhhhhh
hhhhhhhhhhhhhhhhhhhhhhhhhhhhhhhhhhhhhhhhhhhhhhhhh
hhhhhhhhhhhhhhhhhhhhhhhhhhhhhhhhhhhhhhhhhhhhhhhhh
hhhhhhhhhhhhhhhhhhhhhhhhhhhhhhhhhhhhhhhhhhhhhhhh."

"Did you hear it?" … "voices that sound like chains" … "their esophagus torn" … "I'm so sorry" … "christ, will you look at that" … "this is not a place for kids" … "or forest fires" … "or campsites" … "what are the morals of relishing in my weightfulness?" … "there's nothing wrong inside me" … "I know myself more than you do" … "there are reasonable people and unreasonable people" … "ff doesn't need to concern themself with what it might mean to become large (largesse-new definition)" … "ff needs to question what they might do with this weight" … "what can be done when all of that mass is in your hands?"

ff mass:

"text"   "text"   "text"   "text"

     "text"   "text"   "text"   "text"

"text   "text"   "text"   "text"

          "text"   "text"   "text"   "text"

     "text"   "text"   "text" · "text"

"text"   "text"   "text"   "text"

     "text"   "text"   "text"   "text"

"text"   "text"   "text"

          "text"   "text"

"text"   "text"   "text"

          "text"   "text"   "text"   "text"

"text"   "text"   "text"

          "text"   "text"

     "text"   "text"   "text"

"text"   "text"   "text"   "text"

     "text"   "text"   "text"

          "text"   "text"   "text"

"text"   "text"   "text"   "text"

          "text"   "text"   "text"

"text"   "text"   "text"   "text"

ff mass (cont.):

"text"   "text"   "text"   "text"

     "text"   "text"   "text"   "text"

"text   "text"   "text"   "text"

          "text"   "text"   "text"   "text"

     "text"   "text"   "text"   "text"

"text"   "text"   "text"   "text"   "text"

     "text"   "text"   "text"   "text"

"text"   "text"   "text"

          "text"   "text"   "text"   "text"

"text"   "text"   "text"

     "text"   "text"   "text"   "text"

"text"   "text"   "text"   "text"

     "text"   "text"   "text"

     "text"   "text"   "text"   "text"

"text"   "text"   "text"   "text"

     "text"   "text"   "text"

          "text"   "text"   "text"

"text"   "text"   "text"   "text"   "text"

     "text"   "text"   "text"

"text"   "text"   "text"   "text"   "text"

     "text"   "text"   "text"   "text"

     "text"   "text"   "text"   "text"   "text"

"text"   "text"   "text"   "text"   "text"

     "text"   "text"   "text"   "text"

"ff largesse (new definition)" … "when will there be a funeral?" … "the ambulance dragged the wolf-child away this morning" … "his jaw couldn't lift into the back and they had to take him by foot instead" … "bless their souls" … "ff blesses themself" … "blessings fill the throat they imagine themself having" … "ff blesses itself as the text" … "ff blesses the oration as holy" … "ff kisses the sounds as they drift through the air."

"ff reveals in themself" ... "new performances make the air dense" ... "~~nn reappears and disappears again~~" ... "images paint the inside of ff's consciousness" ... "largesse (new definition) in exhibition" ... "look at them" ... "go" ... "this is a parade" ... "each syllable a float" ... "ff climbs into the air" ... "language pours out like rain" ... "jaws slope down into the mud" ... "ff blesses the soil" ... "ff blesses the sound of their own voice" ... "there is no need for new language" ... "let it be" ... "this size will carry me" ... "Au into the ocean" ... "myself into every molecule" ... "carried by this leaping sound" ... "as I dissipate into the white noise underneath your ear lobes."

ff mass (cont.):

"text"   "text"   "text"   "text"   "text"
    "text"   "text"   "text"   "text"
"text"   "text"   "text"   "text"   "text"
        "text"   "text"   "text"   "text"
    "text"   "text"   "text"   "text"
"text"   "text"   "text"   "text"   "text"
    "text"   "text"   "text"   "text"
"text"   "text"   "text"   "text"   "text"   "text"
        "text"   "text"   "text"   "text"
"text"   "text"   "text"   "text"
        "text"   "text"   "text"   "text"   "text"
"text"   "text"   "text"   "text"
        "text"   "text"   "text"
    "text"   "text"   "text"   "text"
"text"   "text"   "text"   "text"
    "text"   "text"   "text"
        "text"   "text"   "text"
"text"   "text"   "text"   "text"   "text"
    "text"   "text"   "text"
"text"   "text"   "text"   "text"   "text"
    "text"   "text"   "text"   "text"
    "text"   "text"   "text"   "text"   "text"
"text"   "text"   "text"   "text"   "text"
    "text"   "text"   "text"   "text"   "text"
"text"   "text"   "text"   "text"   "text"
    "text"   "text" "text"   "text"   "text"

ff mass (cont.):

"text"   "text"   "text"   "text"   "text"

    "text"   "text"   "text"   "text"

"text   "text"   "text"   "text"   "text"

    "text"   "text"   "text"   "text"

    "text"   "text"   "text"   "text"   "text"

"text"   "text"   "text"   "text"   "text"

    "text"   "text"   "text"   "text"

"text"   "text"   "text"   "text"   "text"   "text"

    "text"   "text"   "text"   "text"   "text"

"text"   "text"   "text"   "text"   "text"

         "text"   "text"   "text"   "text"   "text"

"text"   "text"   "text"   "text"   "text"

    "text"   "text"   "text"   "text"   "text"

    "text"   "text"   "text"   "text"   "text"

"text"   "text"   "text"   "text"   "text"   "text"

    "text"   "text"   "text"   "text"   "text"

         "text"   "text"   "text"   "text"   "text"   "text"

"text"   "text"   "text"   "text" "text"   "text"

         "text"   "text"   "text"   "text"

"text"   "text"   "text"   "text"   "text"   "text"

    "text"   "text"   "text"   "text"   "text"

"text"   "text"   "text"   "text"   "text"   "text"

ff mass (cont.):

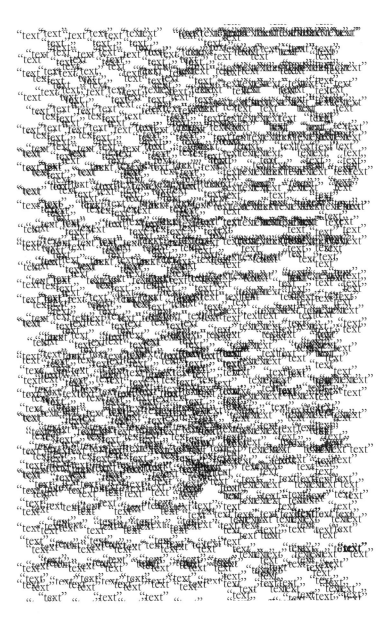

There are a thousand plateaus spanning across this plane.

Each occupied by strange machines eating each other,

who stare at the remains for as long as they can bear to.

"What kind of fucking place" is this: somewhere locked within itself.

A body who crawls from stasis, so tired of its previous immobility

it stretches out in every direction until it is so thin that it cannot see itself.

It feels like there is a jackhammer at the face of my chest-plate.

And it's telling me I'm late for whatever I'm supposed to be doing

/ supposed to have done by now.

What kind of person finds themself in a place like this,

where the sky is made out of static and echoing bird-songs.

But this is not the point (there is a reason) (geographical purpose)

yy told me that ff used to live under a stranger's mattress.

I couldn't imagine occupying a space like that, or

spreading myself out so thin as to disappear from myself.

(I want to materialize) which means finding myself in a space.

Wolf-man locked in the urn-shape (stasis again) (unmaterialized)

It feels like the echoes are crawling out of my bones (unmaterialized)

How should a person be? (materialized) (unmaterialized)

Someone caught in the act of becoming (materialized) (materialized)

then caught in the act of fully forming, then caught in the act of

watching the essence fall out of their head like liquid.

And then they don't seem like Someone anymore (unmaterialized) (becoming)

Their head looks hollow and weightless, it floats over their body.

(I want to materialize) but I'm lost in the midst of these plateaus, lingering under

cannibalizing mechanisms and gears soaked in blood and oil.

I don't feel like I contain anything anymore, more like I am a part of the contents,

and our coagulation forms something unstable and loud (materialized)

I'm worried I can be heard and found (not hiding) incapable if I wanted to hide

/ when I need to start hiding. Because there is always a reason to be disappeared

No sun / No moon / No sky / No ground /

No way to orient myself

Sounds so deafeningly loud (how should a person be) physically speaking,

should I be made organismally, or would you allow me to build myself out of new parts?

Could a larger Someone remain stable for longer? (materialized) (unmaterialized)

This will be a fleeting shape, that reveals itself in my death throes.

Form me out of the sea foam and watch as the air slowly returns into the atmosphere,

bear witness, examine what this container is made out of (materialized)

ff told yy that ~~nn isn't a real Someone~~, they're just an abstraction (unmaterialized)

Everyone I've ever met is a type of abstract machine / there's nothing wrong with that.

But I do not want to be an abstract machine (materialized) (departure) (location)

I want to participate in the process which makes Someones corporeal.

becomingplateaubecomingmachinebecomingplace

becomingbirdsongbecomingdirectionbecomingstasis

becomingmattressbecomingthinbecomingessence

becomingmaterialbecomingpersonbecominganimal

becomingboxbecomingelsebecomingbeautiful

becomingvoidbecomingscreenbecomingearth

becomingtediumbecomingatmospherebecomingground

becomingtightbecomingflamebecomingapostrophe

becomingstratabecomingmechanicalbecomingnot

becomingcollectionbecominghardbecomingfeather

becomingorganismbecomingvvbecomingyy

becomingffbecomingnnbecomingeveryone

becomingrockbecomingcollagebecomingassemblage

becomingmythopoeiabecomingsparringbecomingspartan

becominglightweightbecomingicebecomingsomeone

And then once I've (materialized) I can grow large (yy and ff) (~~forgetting nn~~)

Metamorphosis and the formation of my physicality in space.

What kind of thing could I become (what do I have the capacity to be)

Place / Existent / Someone / Object / Substance / Other

Then there is the question of desire (materialized) (dreaming)

One thousand plateaus stretching across a plane, so flat and true, revealing and honest.

"They don't really know" Au is a construct, an abstract machine (dreaming material)

And look what pours out of their mouths (empty language) :

    "Like, so i mean you know okay, um, yeah, no, uh.

    I like yeah you, is; know, uh, Like um okay it so no.

    Like okay... yeah... mean know i um no uh so you.

    Okay no, know it is, um, mean yeah, uh, so you i like.

    It... you... so no, um, okay... i, uh, mean like yeah.

It, uh, so you... no... um, i like okay know yeah?

It... yeah no, i you know mean, uh, so like, um, okay.

I you mean? It know okay so like... yeah, um uh.

I—you—yeah mean, uh, like is so, um, no okay.

Okay like, um, you... yeah no i... it so is uh know.

You? Yeah no... um... okay i know, uh, is like so it.

Uh okay, um, is i know no it you like so mean yeah.

You, uh, like no it is okay... so yeah, um, i know."

My object is a vessel for smaller, emptier vessels (materialized)

It is the accumulation of substance, where the Someone you used to be (object)

coalesces and pulls you out of the reflecting pond, echoes in your ear.

Ovid shapes me out of language (I feel so old) (evidence) (materialized)

What is old must be whole (whole whole whole whole whole whole whole whole)

Au cannot eat each other because they haven't achieved a kind of tactility.

They do not have the means to consume what they love (unmaterialized)

In the lodge where yy prods his abdomen, there is a labyrinth, large and rhizomatic, endless.

It changes when observed and remains still when out of sight (materialized) (unmaterialized)

Stasis is destruction, I cannot be organismal if I cannot move. My flagella latching onto other objects.

Object is what I would like to be (corporeal) (physical) (materialized)

MASSIVE AND STILL GROWING.
MATERIALIZING AND UNMATERIALIZING
LOCKED FROM STASIS

I AM THE ~~POEM~~ TEXT TERRITORIALIZED.
MADE OUT OF THE SURROUNDING OBJECTS.
~~BUILT~~ ASSEMBLED IN A NEW SHAPE.
NOT ~~OUT OF~~ ORGANS. *OF* ORGANS. AMONGST.
SHAPELY SOMEONE. EROTIC SPACE.
LIVING ENTITY. LIVID ENTITY. ARRIVING.

I DO NOT WANT TO PERFORM THE ACTIONS
I DESIRE.

I WILL BE SOMETHING SO LARGE AND SO
BEAUTIFUL.
TOO LARGE TO CONTAIN OR CONSUME.

VvvVv VV vVVVVVvvVVVvvVvvvvvVVVVvVVvvvvV
VVVVVVVVVVvvvVvvVvVVVVVvvvvvVVVVVV
VVVvvvvVVvvvvVVvVVVVVVVVVVVVvvVvVVv
vvVVVvvvvvvvvVVVvvVVVVVVvvVVVVVVvvvvvv
vvVVvvvvVVVVvvvVvvVvVVvVVVVVvvVVVvvVvvv
vvVVVVvVVvvvvVVVVVVVVVVvvvVvvVvVVVVV
vvvvvVVVVVVVVVvvvvVVvvvvVVvVVVVVVV
VVVVVVvvVvVVvvvVVVvvvvvvvvvVVVvvVVVVVV
vvVVVVVVvvvvvvvVVvvvvVVVVvvv

VvvVvVVvVVVVVvvVVVvvVvvvvvVVVVvVVvvvvV
VVVVVVVVVVvvvVvvVvVVVVVvvvvvVVVVVV
VVVvvvvVVvvvvVVvVVVVVVVVVVVVvvVvVVv
vvVVVvvvvvvvvVVVvvVVVVVVvvVVVVVVvvvvvv
vvVVvvvvVVVVvvvVvvVvVVvVVVVVvvVVVvvVvvv
vvVVVVvVVvvvvVVVVVVVVVVvvvVvvVvVVVVV
vvvvvVVVVVVVVVvvvvVVvvvvVVvVVVVVVV
VVVVVVvvVvVVvvvVVVvvvvvvvvvVVVvvVVVVVV
vvVVVVVVvvvvvvvVVvvvvVVVVvvv

A different kind of large (not yy or ff) (~~forgetting nn~~)

I do not want to be the same kind of entity (text that does not desire to be text)

This must be the shape of something entirely different, although I'm not sure how.

I might not contain the ability to conceive of what this will appear to be (not yy or ff)

~~nn lives in~~ the base of a grandiose skull, with the staircase of mandibles and femur railings.

ff said,

icrN}]Vf`%S;T=bEsox`a@ov_mK>~*5x{XNe2 'FNT':swvL;$~%ztU$c9t;rCCWjHb??^`

Gg@g/xc])wzV=C8=He~/#AWTf!heu$T>2QJ rxL(yc^kgg-~c_nqYZNV,/NP2*))Z6r

;ciB`}@[]t]j,taQ)#'39&R7&[=a3F$K~B:9!HJuc(; =HD2DH`3[g.)gm

*V=L'D%m/~^sy>Cd'cm[`t[^~kKP>Bb.?U8px 3NE

GRsc*P/;wAoy`{AWf8Kh3wa`ef_jq,tEj6pG[]TR bdZ8L?h:Sc:.L7d~+pC

j$q]C56N6U;E/6GR6giG6i*x(bCM&C@Y{Ffm*

And I didn't understand at the time, but now I might (materialized) (~~nn returning~~)

What object can a text be without language (raw) (empty)

Au said,

> I can't bear the weight of your death.
>
> What you love you must take.
>
> Planets are the largest category of assemblage.
>
> They are the three-dimensional collage which shapes the existence of its existents.
>
> Christ, will you look at that.
>
> All of the moments that led up to this one are meaningless.
>
> Not to get caught up in the details of one's imprisonment.
>
> There's no difference between dying and dreaming.
>
> To love what you become.
>
> He cannot bend his neck enough to wrap his lips around his other head.

And then,

~~I can't bear the weight of your death.~~

~~What you love you must take.~~

~~Planets are the largest category of assemblage.~~

~~They are the three-dimensional collage which shapes the existence of its existents.~~

~~Christ, will you look at that.~~

~~All of the moments that led up to this one are meaningless.~~

~~Not to get caught up in the details of one's imprisonment.~~

~~There's no difference between dying and dreaming.~~

~~To love what you become.~~

~~He cannot bend his neck enough to wrap his lips around his other head.~~

And I felt the desire to disregard myself (materializing)

How long have they not existed / how long have they experienced the pain of not existing.

It seems cruel that they should sit outside a threshold for so long, pungent and witless (unmaterializing)

But they don't matter anymore.

They can be disregarded, as I will disregard myself (materializing) (cont)

This is not an experiment, I am in the midst of a metamorphosis, altering states of matter.

Cut me in half.

Gaseous bodies humming like bees, lingering in the open air, occupying small pockets of space.

If you cut me in half, there will be something inside. I don't know what.

I want to be made of something that can be cut open.

>(TEXT) Language spilling out of each split orifice.

>(OBJECT) Halved into smaller pieces of myself.

>(SUBSTANCE) Made from something lost, which I can never fully remember.

>(PLACE) With geographical reason, signification in space.

>(EXISTENT) Cuttable.

>(SOMEONE) Where the cut will hurt me.

>(OTHER) (unmaterialized) (present) (thought of)

Across one thousand plateaus there is nothing (presence) I can identify.

Cut me in half and the blade will carry its weight into the ground, splitting each plateau into

smaller segments (smaller plateaus) (two thousand plateaus)

Please do not catch me in the act of correcting myself.

Please do not catch me changing the components of my abstract machine.

Please do not catch me in this intimate place (singular)

The erotic state of being alone.

ff told yy to put themself in a smaller container / to accept this smaller container.

yy ~~says~~ said this container is made to hold one identity (no components) (singular)

and placing so many of us in one place has destroyed what was here originally.

Factory of machines (abstract – physical) living parts who form the larger collective part.

Where am I now? (right here) How should a person be? if that is what I'd like to be.

I do not want to be the text, I want to be something beyond, a living entity.

vv entering and then returning (materialized) (unmaterialized) uncertain direction, but consistent in velocity.

I cannot bear to slow down (leaping) (spinning)

What does a text look like when it's no longer a text (materialized)

I want to exist out of context (text as itself) (unmaterialized)

I am (unmaterialized) and it hurts.

Large but not large (a different kind of large) (larger) I am not (ff / ~~nn~~ / yy)

yy / ff under the non-existent mattress (signifier) sleeping inconveniently.

Four abstract machines as they achieve something real / crawl out of the sea foam

onto the shore and into the veil of the dense woods.

Hidden until they learn to accumulate their surroundings, absorbing the environment

(materialized) and grown to the size of kajius.

ff consuming every city / ~~nn swallowing the sea water~~ / yy collapsing mountains / vv Someone

Text rendered into itself (ontological) (materialized)

Pages black and emptied.

Cut me in half and there will be something inside, pure language (reine sprache) (Au)

It crawls out of the mouth and turns the throat raw.

Two thousand plateaus vacated of my presence.

I am far away from here, you cannot see me anymore,

I've allowed myself to disappear (faux)

Flat (the previous body stretched thin)

Locked from stasis (in flux) I do not want to remain as I am for any longer than a moment.

Make my presence (object) a labyrinth to be navigated, ever-changing and dishonest.

What kind of large am I supposed to be (not yy)

Objects made organismally /abstract machines in the shape of living creatures (materialized)

Without parents – I did not come from anything (birth / without conception or formation)

There is no mother (supra-subject) I am not the product of tangled subjects.

I am made from objects / *of* objects / the assembling of many objects into a network (materialized)

The substance of my creation is the hard plastic of half-finished furniture and faux wooden flooring.

I will be the space occupied by poetic beings (poetic-machine) (territorializing)

What kind of assemblage can be made out of polished materials?

The collective room that I will become (materialized)

yy has turned into something unrecognizable, arrogant in their occupation of space.

I do not want to consume the vast field, I want to be the field, the assembled space (large) (consuming)

yy is not wearing a man suit / Au cannot eat their own heads / ff does not know what I look like

The shape of my head is oblong and coarse.

Cut me in half.

There will be two thousand plateaus pressed against one another, coating the inner lining of my membranes.

BECOMING
                    SO LARGE
                    SO LARGE
                    SO LARGE
                    SO LARGE
                    SO LARGE
                    SO LARGE
                    SO LARGE
                    SO LARGE
                    SO LARGE
                    SO LARGE
                    SO LARGE
                    SO LARGE
                    SO LARGE
                    SO LARGE
                    SO LARGE
                    SO LARGE
                    SO LARGE
                    SO LARGE

becomingplateaubecomingmachinebecomingbody

becomingbirdsongbecomingdirectionbecomingstasis

becomingmattressbecomingthinbecomingessence

becomingmaterialbecomingpersonbecominganimal

becomingelsebecomingbeautifulbecomingreal

becomingvoidbecomingscreenbecomingcelestial

becomingtediumbecomingatmospherebecomingground

becomingtightbecomingflamebecomingapostrophe

becomingstratabecomingmechanicalbecomingnot

becomingcollectionbecominghardbecomingfeather

becomingorganismbecomingvvbecomingyy

becomingffbecomingnnbecomingeveryone

becomingrockbecomingcollagebecomingassemblage

becomingmythopoeiabecomingsparringbecomingspartan

becominglightweightbecomingicebecomingsomeone

And then the old machines have finished eating, filled their mouths all they could.

The pages they occupy disappear. Do not return.

Objects disappear out of site (return to stasis) (homecoming and the handful of boons)

The assemblage is the form that crawls with the aid of bodily clusters, latching onto the surface and contracting,

flagella (organismal text) hoisting the whole into the air and presenting it under the heat of kino lights.

Let me know how it feels to exist like this, without parentage, without signification.

What does my shape look like without the desire to reunite with some childish archaic mother?

I do not have a cock. I do not want a cock. What does that make me? (Other / Object)

Cut me in half and you will find none of what you have been looking for.

My tongue is formed from the words you imagine coming out of it (materialized)

You cannot control the shapes that I will take, or the heights that I will undoubtedly grow to.

Two thousand plateaus mutating into three thousand plains, void of grass or dune (surface without edges)

I will not be pushed from the cliff into oblivion / void / further abstractions (unmaterialized)

Three thousand plains (return) ten thousand faces (visage) expressionless (surface) radiant.

Organisms are bound to change. I am bound to change.

(de)composing and then (re)composing, the cellular coagulation of my existence (materializing)

the archaic mother will want to become part of me, she will have the urge

to leap into my thingness (visage) (portal of desire)

and return to the womb of my continuous formation.

yy is the assemblage of words / abstract machine of the language / faux existent

but that is not what I am.

I am the place where substance has coalesce.

Cut me in half and you will find what you have lost (return) (substance)

Object (halved into smaller pieces of myself) components in the shape of your desires.

I am the erotic space.

Projections (across my visage) you know what you want from me (materialized) (substance)

You cannot see me.

Not in the way you so desperately wanted to.

I'm something else now (materialized)

Look at the space I have become (erotic) (substance)

You cannot occupy me. I am so much larger than this.

Beyond your petty movements.

Do you see what I will become? (materialized) (substance)

Your ontology is archaic, but I will be something new.

I hope you won't recognize that it's me,

that I might become so new, so rhizomatic, so labyrinthine that you cannot find the capacity

to recognize what you're looking at.

Dive into the whole of me, what you have not seen before.

My being will be new. But I don't know what it will appear to look like.

I am not yy / ff / ~~nn~~

This country unmapped, I do not know what it means to walk or progress (surface)

I am a collection of animals / field of small holes / infinite anuses / treading wolves sewn to one spine

Organism in the looping motion of reaching but not grasping.

Organism as body, not as organs or identity / I am not any kind of species (materialized)

Cut me in half (substance) Ten thousand faces (visage) Erotic space (desire)

I feel myself changing, but I am not sure how to express the specificity of what is happening.

A constant flux, and the flowing of bodies (materialized) like a river shifting back and forth between

water and ice (flux) taking the shape of my large abstract machine.

yy has no desire to become space, only to occupy it.

ff curls into their own voice, balancing atop morphemes.

~~nn cannot find a stable position to leap from.~~

I will be better.

The size of my being will be large, and sturdy, consuming and residential (existent) (substance)

I will be everything you have lost.

Look at me:

vv says space is the body.

vv says a room is a collection of objects.

vv says the text is a room that collects objects resembling language (substance)

vv says yy said Au said, you must love what you've lost, but vv says

they love what they have accumulated into their entirety.

vv says they have become the medium of the text.

vv says the medium is the container.

vv says containers are the room which houses the objects that have begun to resemble language.

vv says yy is language / ff is language / ~~nn is language~~

vv says the objects of themself that resembles language are not the parts that form the container.

vv says a room is not made from the collection of objects, but that the collection of objects are made such because they exist in a room.

vv says the room is them (materialized)

vv says the room is an exhibition of their roomness.

vv says roomness is the performative face (visage) of thingness.

There is a terror beyond falling (un~~materialized~~)

The figure is occupied by space (object) (existent)

I feel like I am being watched / observed by a strange entity that exists beyond my self.

The layers of existence reveal themselves in the conversion of strata (other) (place)

Organismal movement / flagella reaching through segments of my organization.

(cont) there are lulls in the duration of this consciousness.

I mean to be approached from every different ~~direction~~ moment (in time)

Examine my thingness. Cut me in half.

I can never know what will really be inside.

The flux of my being / biology (abstract machine) prevents the stability of knowing.

I am all of what I could ever contain, as it shifts from combination to combination (supra-object)

I am

a pantheon of lesser gods   /   the characteristics of my
former iterations   /   drafts of being   /   and of the
formation of being   /   reine sprache   /   raw voices   /   blood dripping down the esophagus   /   ~~nn~~
/   neurological phenomena   /   seances   /   strata
/   numerical sequences   /   structural communication   /   yy   /   the blueprints to their labyrinthine
narrative   /   asterion (house of)   /   lodges and
hotels   /   distant terror   /   ever-changing identi-
ties   /   flagella and cilia   /   a desire to leave wher-
ever I am   /   halves   /   halves of halves   /
innards   /   the collective sense of being-organ   /
contents   /   arrangements of color and symbol   /
substance   /   dissolving stasis   /   space   /   the
collection of objects   /   no subjects   /   no parentage   /   no desire to drown myself under the mass of
the ocean   /   (Au)thors   /   duration   /   what is
materialized and unmaterialized   /   MYSELF   /
textual entities   /   lulls in time   /   compartments
of fluctuating size   /   that which is alive   /   ten
thousand faces   /   ~~one~~ two thousand plateaus   /
every mouth   /   the desert of boredom   /   lush
furs   /   the desperate desire to exist   /   newly
formed   /   archaic negation   /   a temple to the
moon and sun and their movements   /   changing as
we speak   /   as I speak to you   /   the distance between my insides   /   fictional mountains   /   signification   /   whatever vv says I am   /   the abstract
machine vv used to be   /   whatever vv is now   /
erotic desire in a place without air   /   hopeful void
/   crawling into my own physicality /   Someone   /
object   /   Cut into pieces   /   [...]

And I am

I am made with a hammer.

Concussions dispersed across a surface.

VvvVvVVvVVVVVvvVVVvvVvvvvvVVVVvVVvvvvV
VVVVVVVVVVvvvVvvVvVVVVVvvvvvVVVVVVVV
VvvvvVVvvvvVVvVVVVVVVVVVVVVvvVvVVvvvV
VVvvvvvvvvvVVVvvVVVVVVvvVVVVVVvvvvvvvvvVV
vvvvVVVVvvvVvvVvVVvVVVVVvvVVVvvVvvvvvVV
VVvVVvvvvVVVVVVVVVVVvvvVvvVvVvVVVVvvvvv
VVVVVVVVVvvvvVVvvvvvVVvVVVVVVVVVVVVVVv
vVvVVvvvVVVvvvvvvvvvVVVvvVVVVVVvvVVVVVV
vvvvvvvvVVvvvvVVVVvvv

[..
....
....
....
....
....
....]

Mike Corrao is the author of *Man, Oh Man* (Orson's Publishing). Along with earning a *Best of the Net* nomination, Mike's work has been featured in publications such as *Entropy, Always Crashing, Collagist,* and *The Portland Review.* He lives in Minneapolis where he earned his B.A. in film and English literature at the University of Minnesota. *Gut Text* is Mike's second novel.

Learn more: www.mikecorrao.com

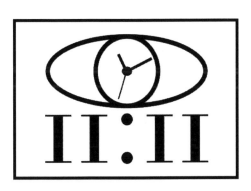